Christmas S[illegible]s for the Flute.

Arranged by Robin De Smet.

Wise Publications
London/New York/Sydney

Exclusive Distributors
Music Sales Limited,
8/9 Frith Street, London, W1V 5TZ, England.
Music Sales Pty. Limited,
120 Rothschild Avenue, Rosebery, NSW 2018, Australia.

ISBN 0.7119.1082.0
Order No. AM 65038

Designed by Pearce Marchbank Studio.
Arranged and compiled by Robin De Smet.

As With Gladness Men Of Old

Traditional

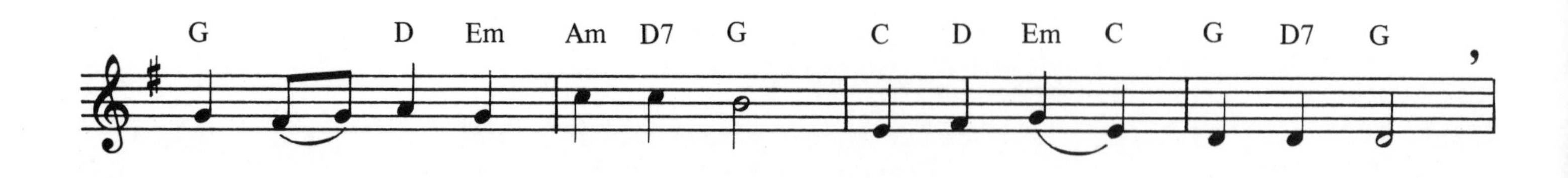

The Jolly Old Man In The Bright Red Suit

Words & Music: Sunny Skylar

F

F7
Fdim
F7
B♭
E♭m
B♭
E♭m
B♭

Dm7
G7
C
G7
C
C♯dim
G7
C7
C9
f

F
C7

E
F

D7
D+
D7
D+
D7
D+
D7
Gm E♭C7
mf

F
Dm
Gm
D7
Gm
C7
F

Away In A Manger

Traditional

Christmas Children

Words & Music: Leslie Bricusse

Am7 D7/A Gm7 C7/G F♯dim/G Gm6 Dm/A Am7 Gm7 Gm/F
A7sus A7 Em7 A7 F G B♭/G♯ A7 Dsus D
A9sus A7 Dmaj7 D6
E7/B Bm7 E7/B Gm/B♭ D/A E7sus E7
A9sus A7 Dm A7sus Dm A7sus Dm Dm/C Dm9/C
B♭maj7 Am7 Gm7 C7 Fmaj9 F6 Fmaj7 B♭maj7 B♭7-5
Am7 D7/A Gm7 C7/G F♯dim/G Gm6 Dm/A Am7 Gm7 Gm/F
A7sus A7 Em7 A7 F G B♭/G♯ A7 A7+ B♭(addC) B♭ D

Christmas Alphabet

Words & Music: Buddy Kaye and Jules Loman

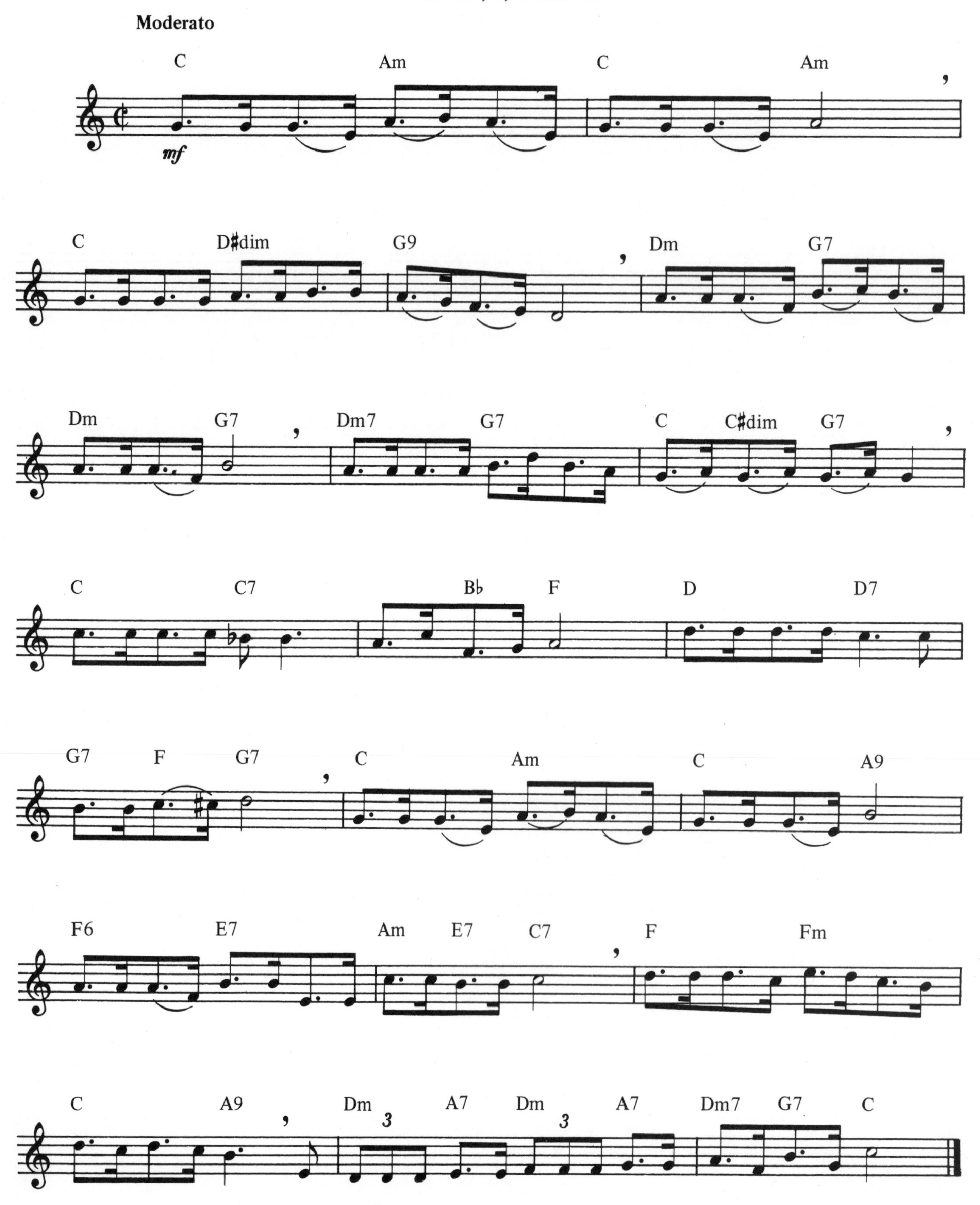

The Boar's Head Carol

Traditional

The Coventry Carol

Traditional

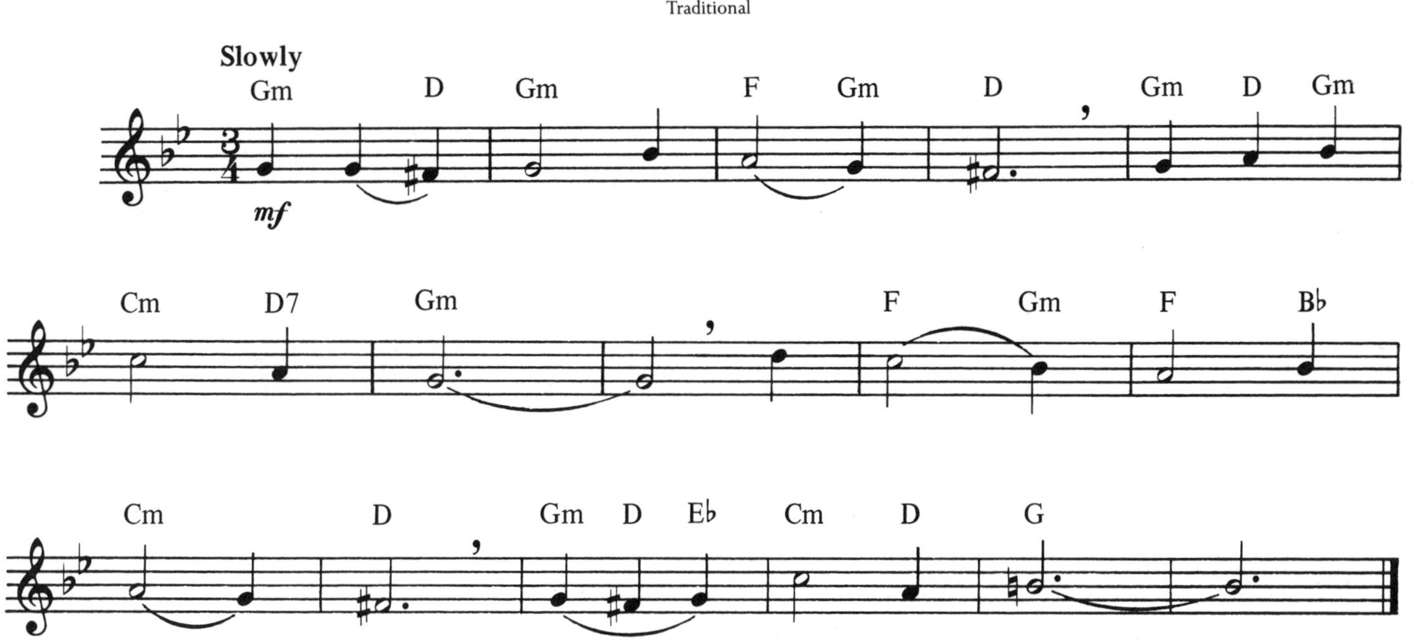

Christmas All Year 'Round

Words: Maddy Russell   Music: Robert Maxwell

Christmas Together

Words & Music: Bill Nicel and Florence Cardell

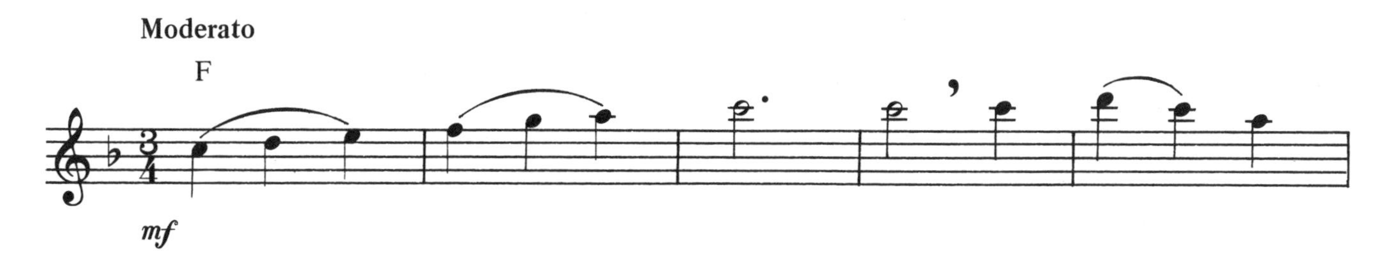

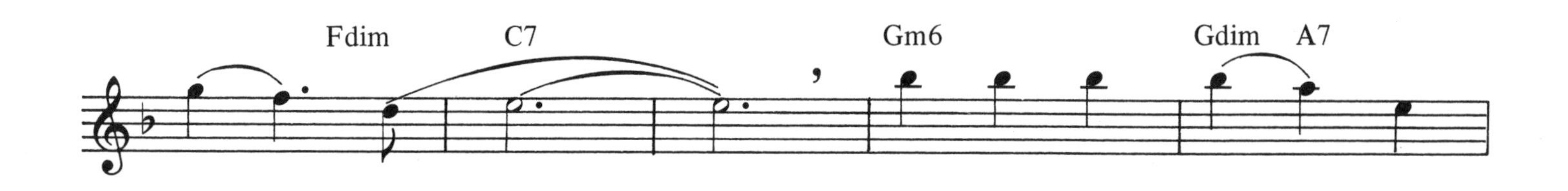

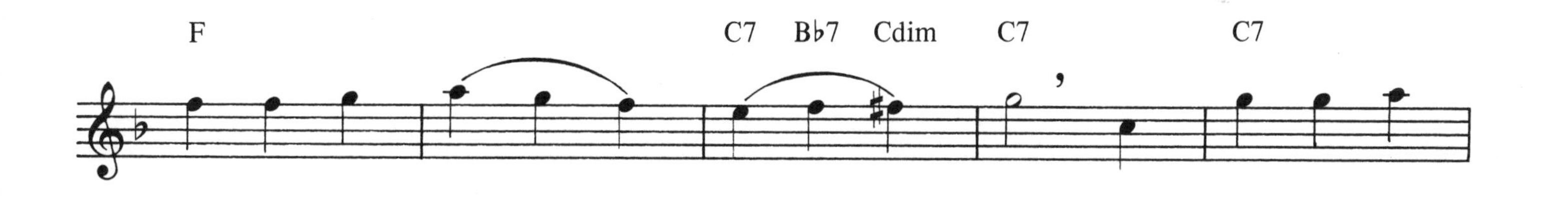

CHRISTMAS

Words: Jenny Lou Carson   Music: Eddy Arnold

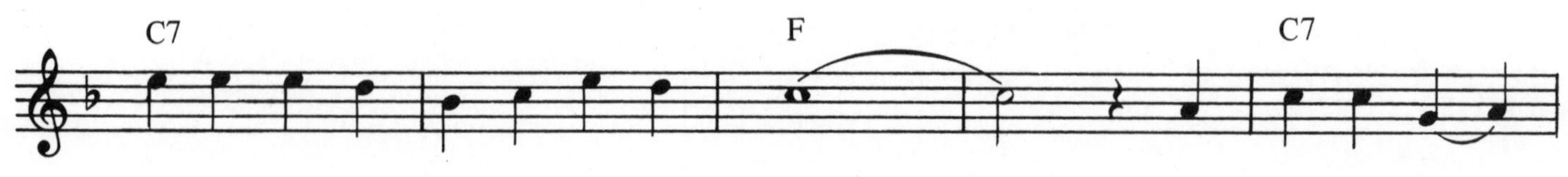

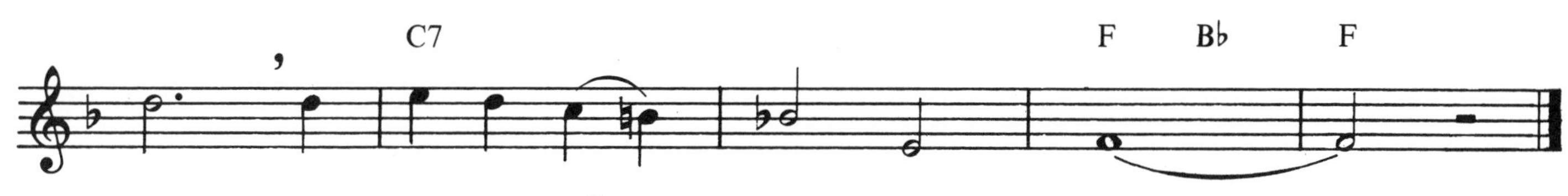

Christmas Bells (a round)

Traditional

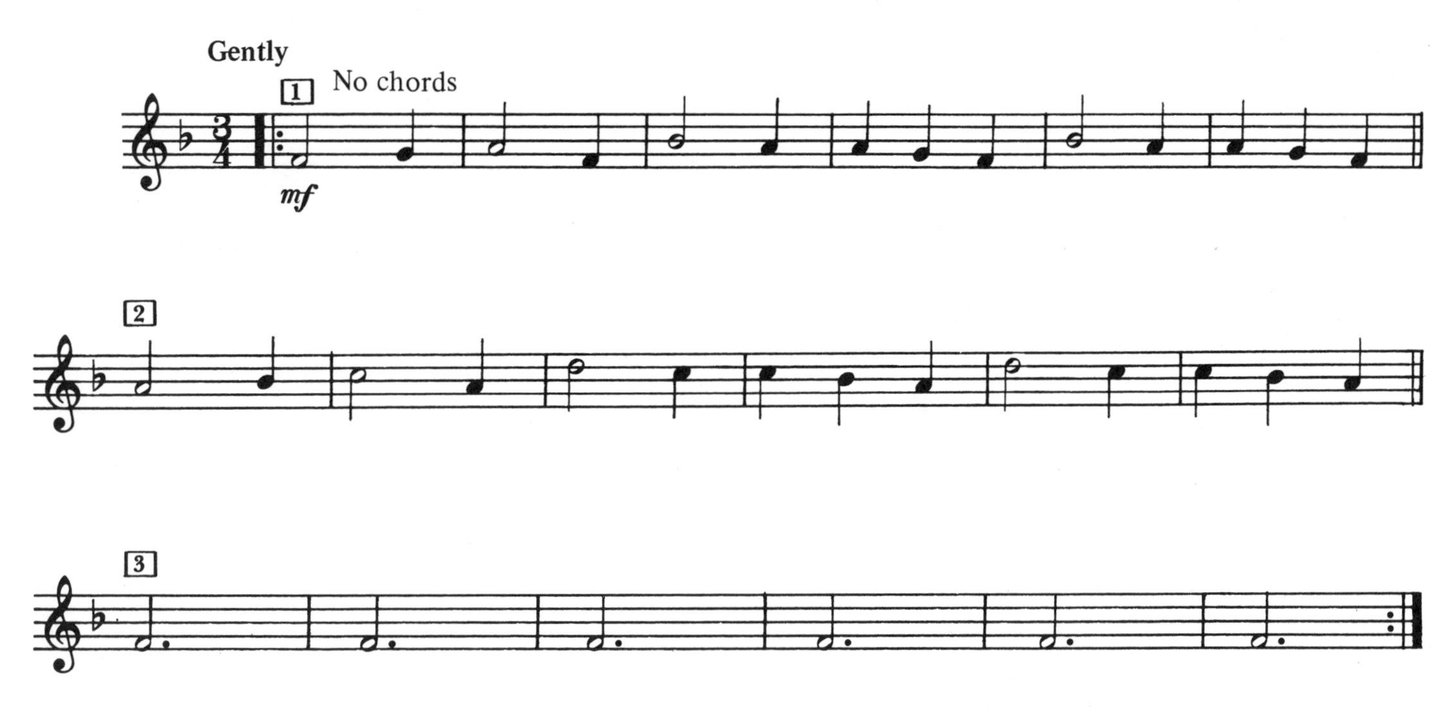

Christmas In Killarney

Words & Music: John Redmond, James Cavanaugh and Frank Weldon

Christmas Candles

Words & Music: Leo Breen and Wilbur Sampson

Christmas And You

Words & Music: Russell Faith and Clarence Way Kehner

Christmas Rock 'N' Roll

Words: Hank Russell Music: Buddy Brooks

Dear Father Christmas

Words & Music: Lawrette Wright

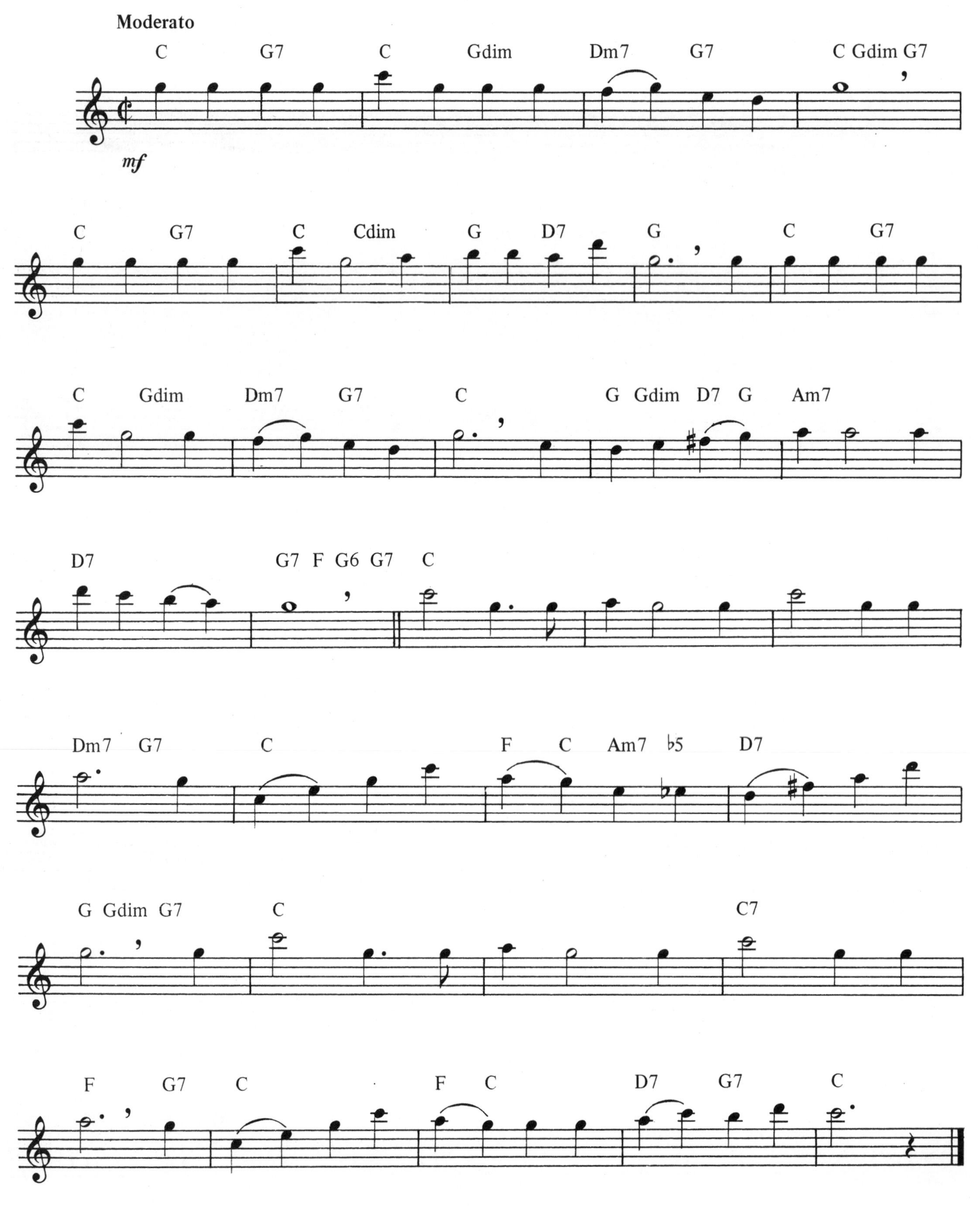

Frosty The Snowman

Words & Music: Steve Nelson and Jack Rollins

The First Nowell

Traditional

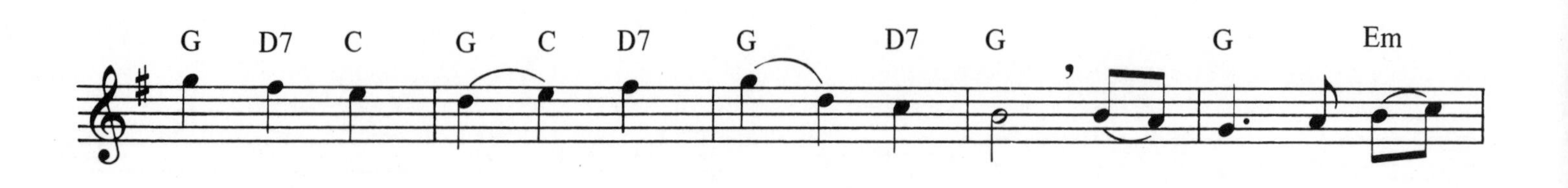

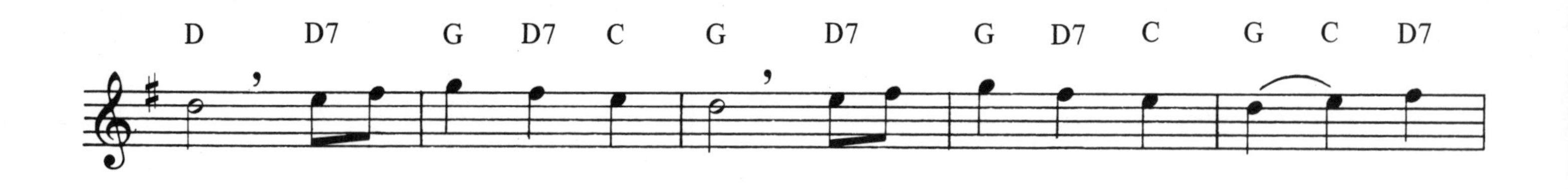

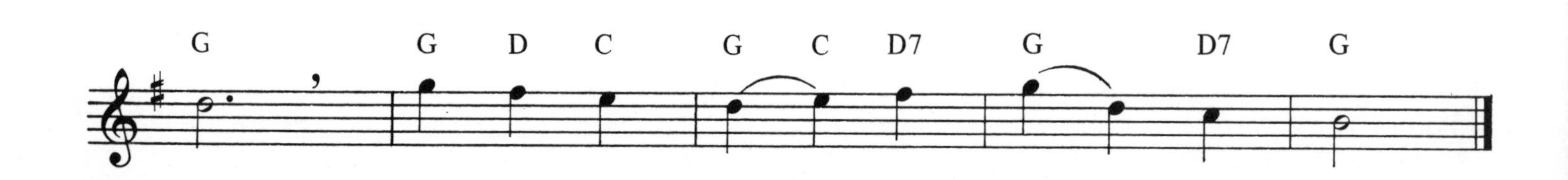

God Rest You Merry Gentlemen

Traditional

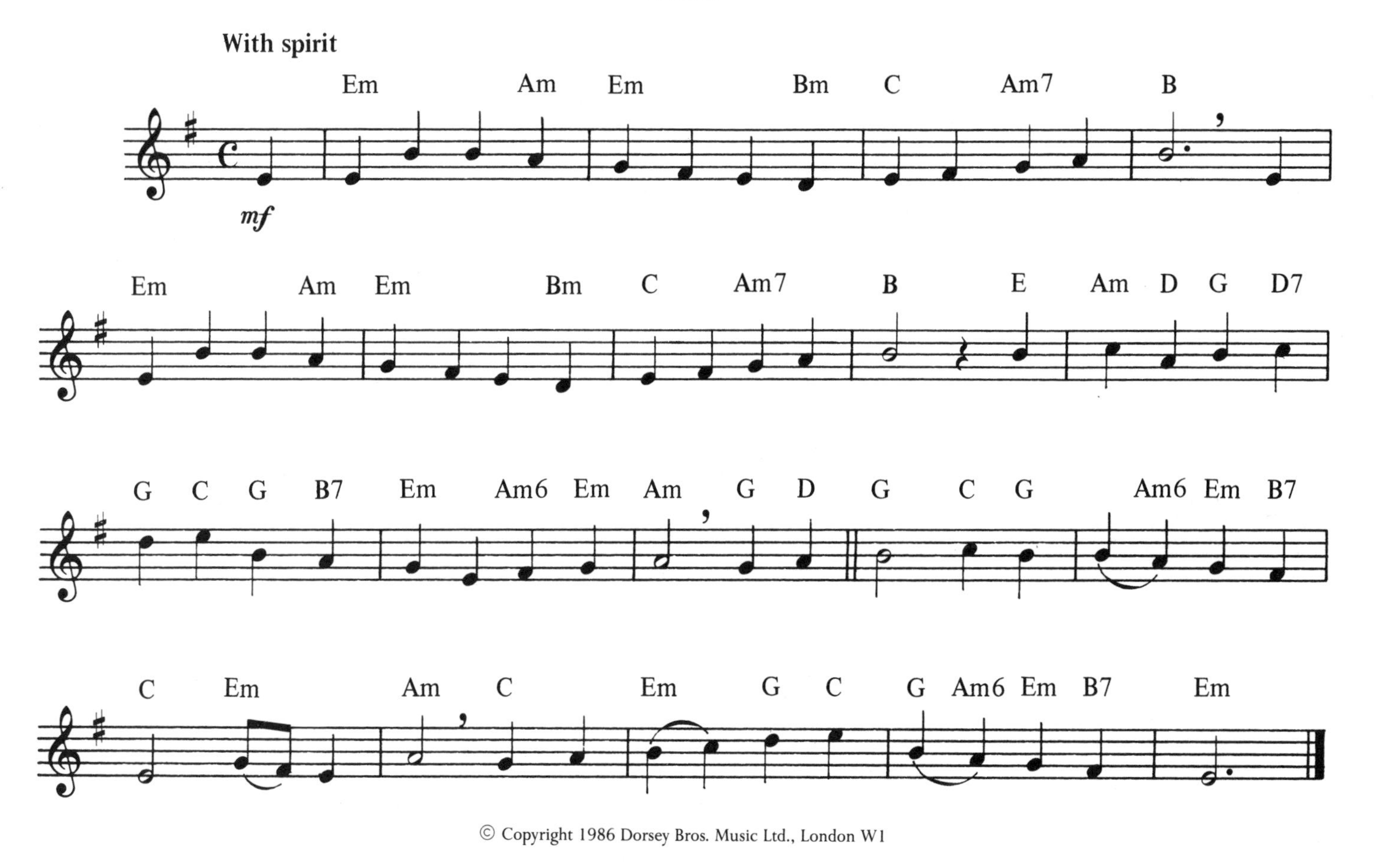

Good King Wenceslas

Traditional

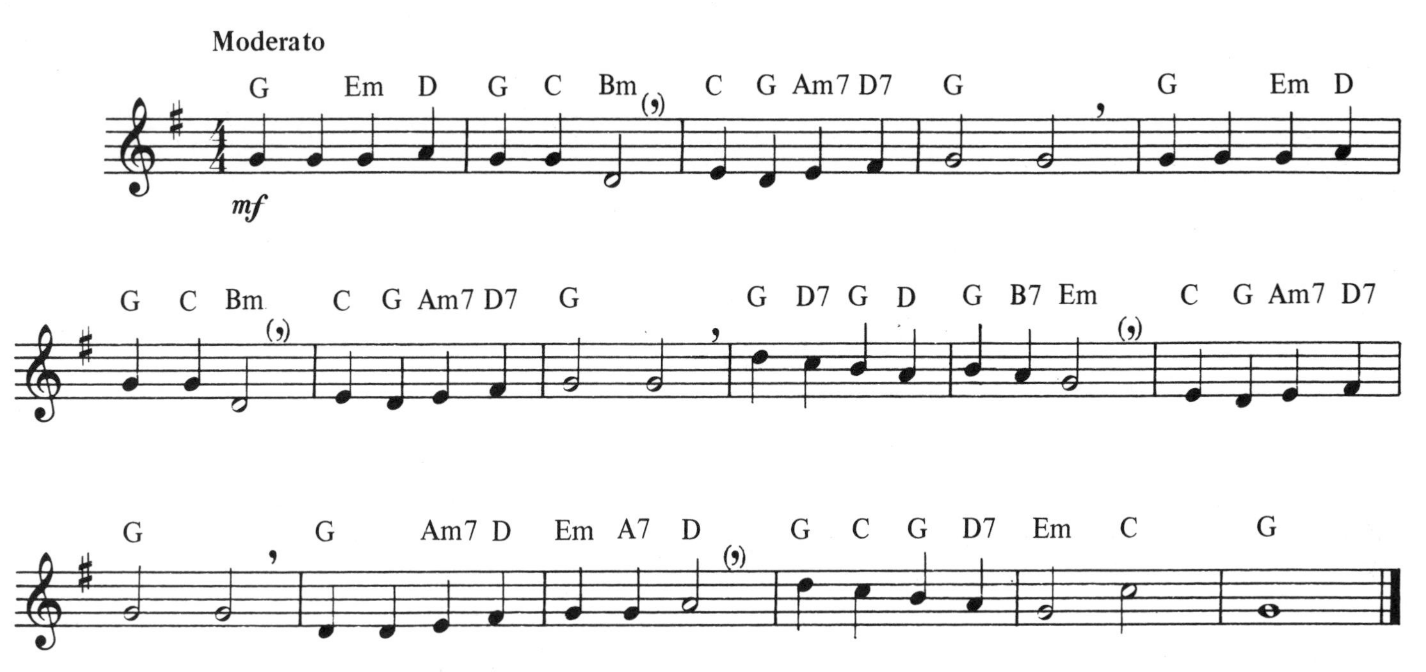

Go Tell It On The Mountain

Traditional

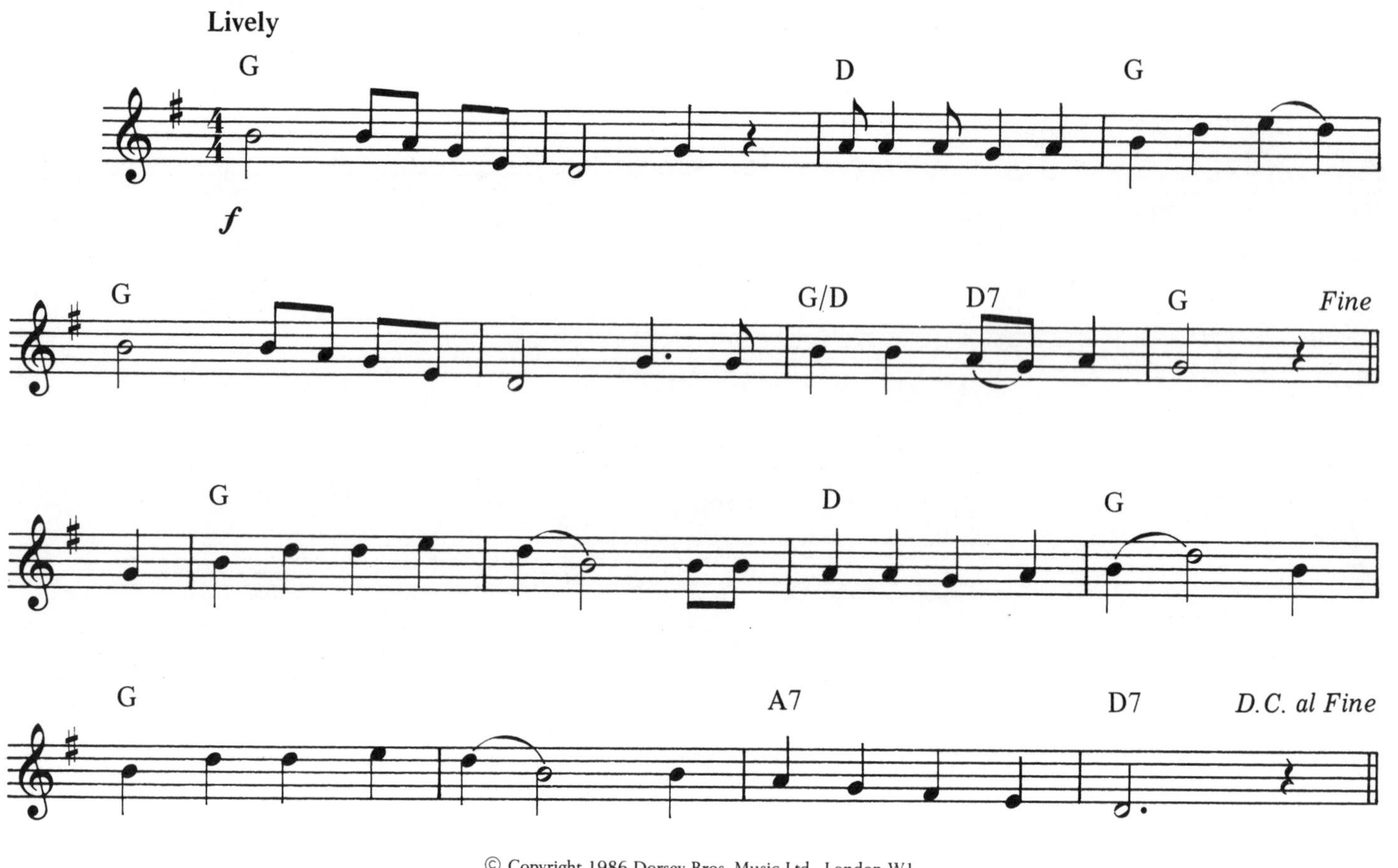

Hark! The Herald Angels Sing

Traditional

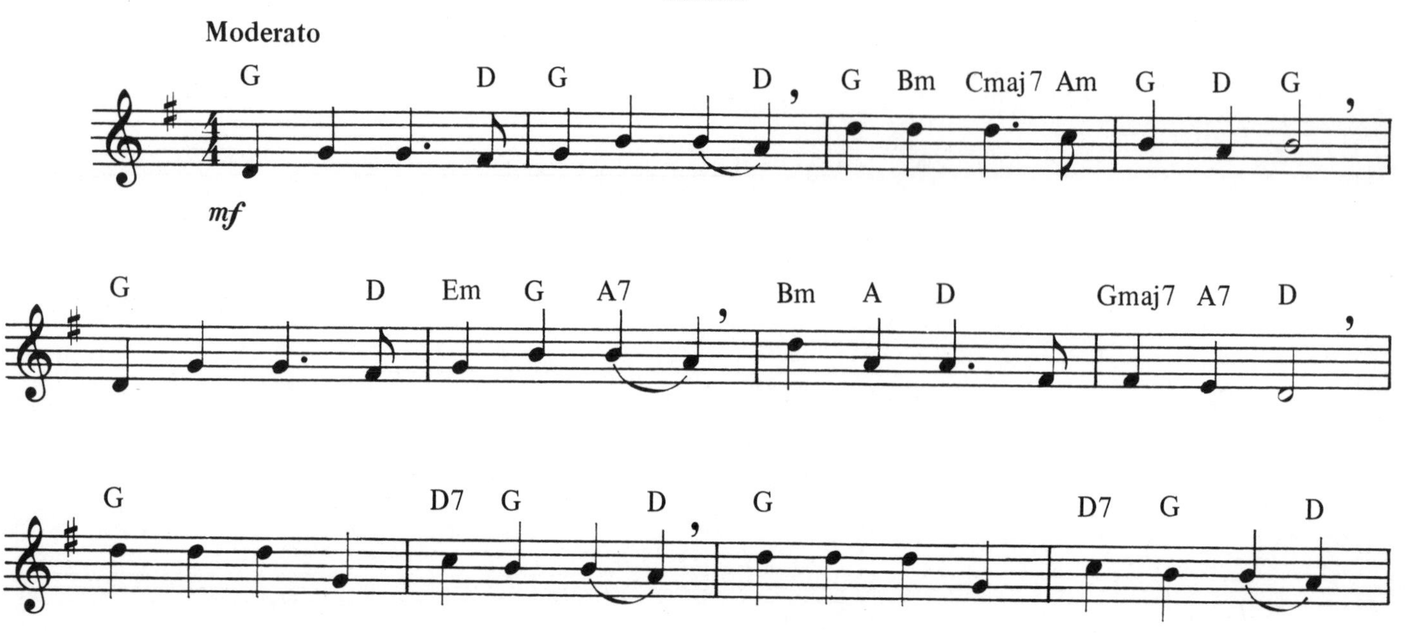

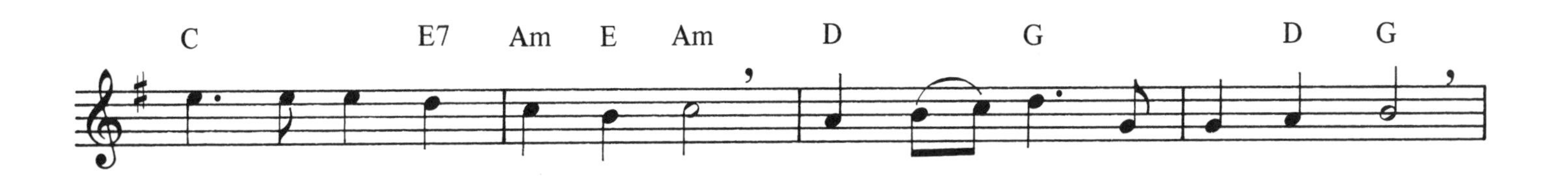

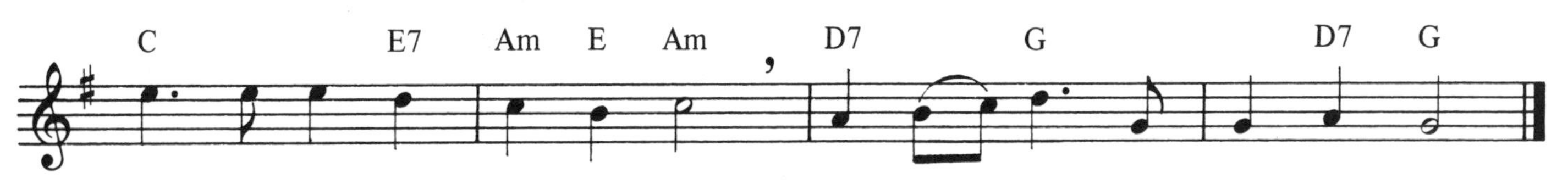

The Huron Carol

Traditional

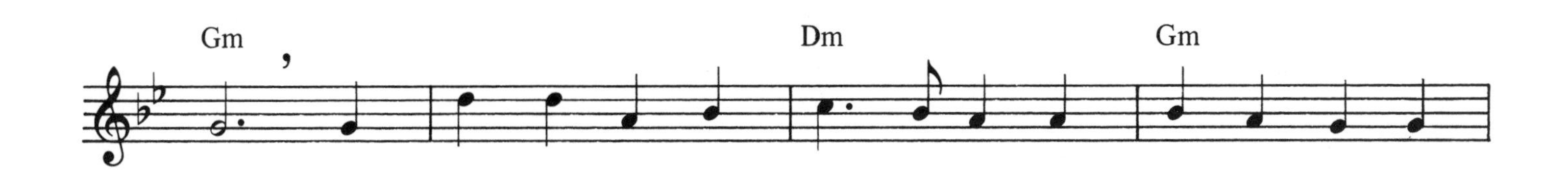

Happy Christmas To You From Me

Words & Music: Lynsey de Paul and Barry Blue

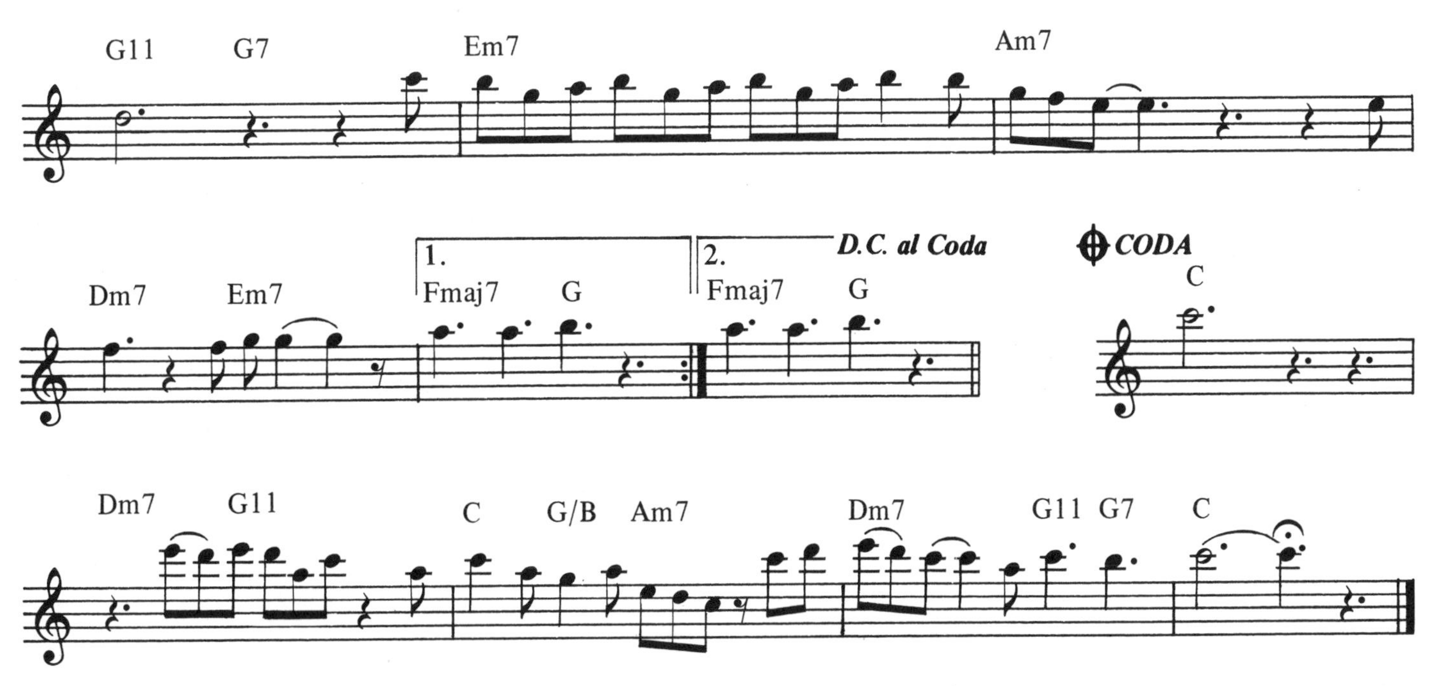

Here We Come A-Wassailing

Traditional

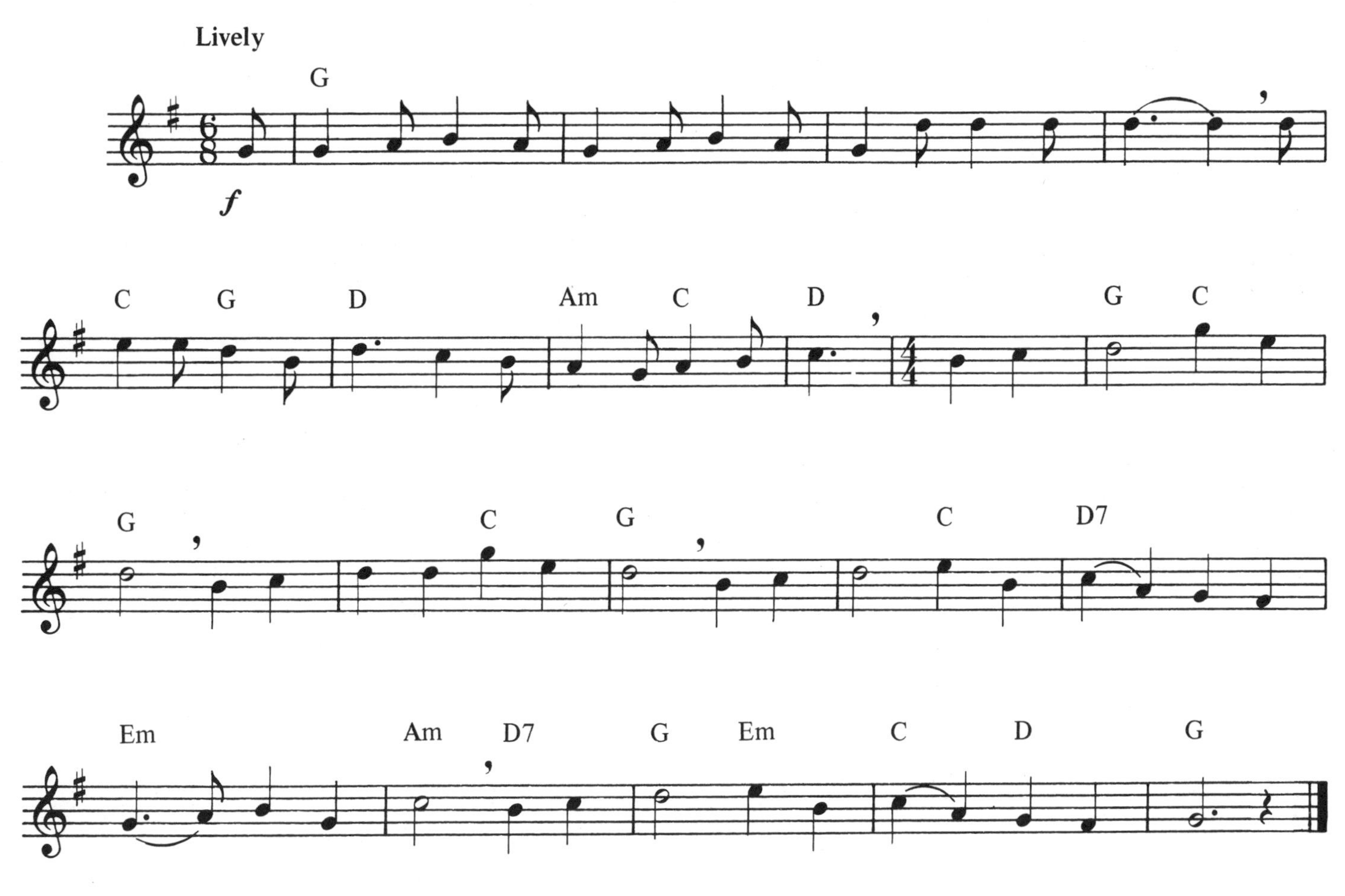

Here Comes Santa Claus

Words & Music: Gene Autry and Oakley Haldeman

The Holly And The Christmas Pud

Words & Music: Michael Treford and Billy Milton

The Holly And The Ivy

Traditional

I Saw Three Ships

Traditional

I Believe In Father Christmas

Words: Peter Sinfield   Music: Greg Lake

I'm Going Home For Christmas

Words & Music: Maurice Sigler, Al Goodhart and Al Hoffman

In Dulci Jubilo

Traditional

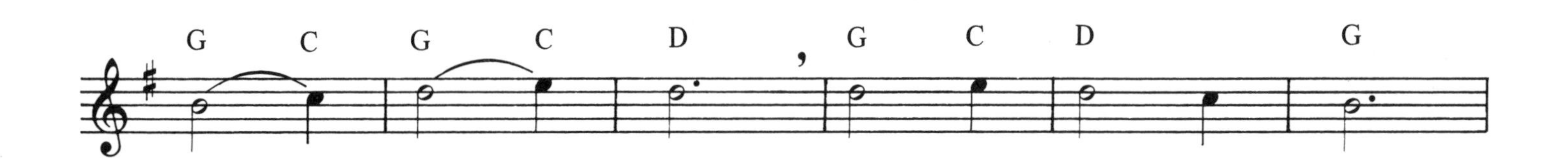

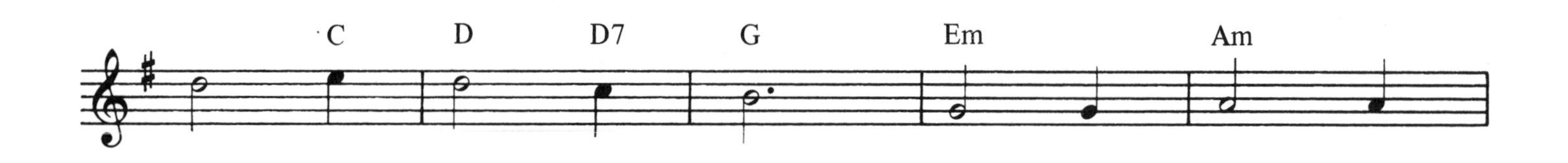

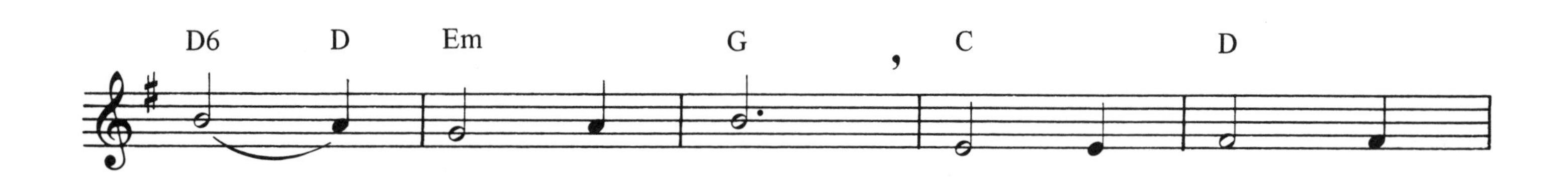

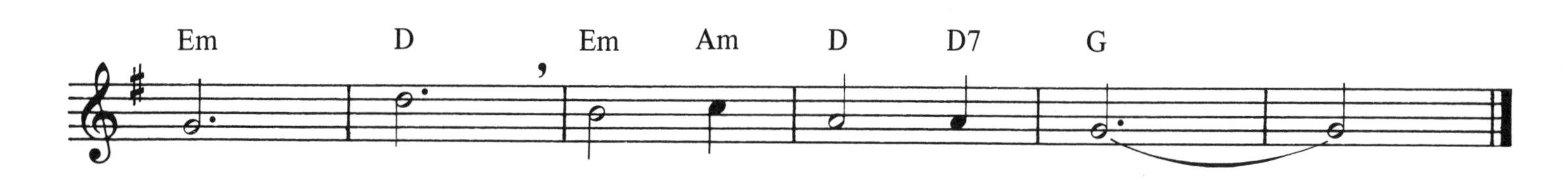

I'm A Little Christmas Cracker

Words & Music: Cosy Lee

A7
3
Dm A7 Dm
B7
3
Em Adim G7
C
G7
G7
G+
C
C7
A7
Dm A7 Dm
D7
G7
C7
D.C. al Coda
CODA
F
C7
B♭
C13
C7
F

Infant Holy

Traditional

Gently
D G
D
G
D7
D
G
mf
D G
D
G
D7
D
G
G C
Am D
G Em
Am D7
G
D7
C
G
D7
C
G

Jolly, Jolly Jingle

Words & Music: Ruth Roberts, Gene Piller and Bill Katz

Jolly Old Saint Nicholas

Words & Music: Vaughn Horton

Jingle Bells

Traditional

Little Jesus (rocking)

Traditional

O Christmas Tree

Traditional

O Come All Ye Faithful

Traditional

Merry Christmas Everybody

Words & Music: Neville Holder and James Lea

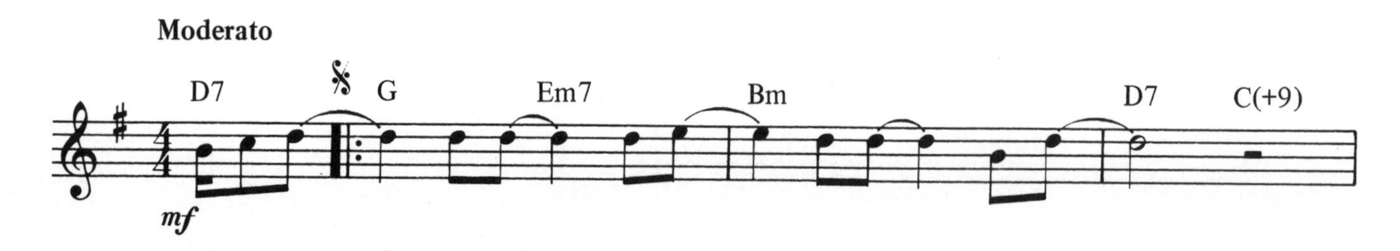

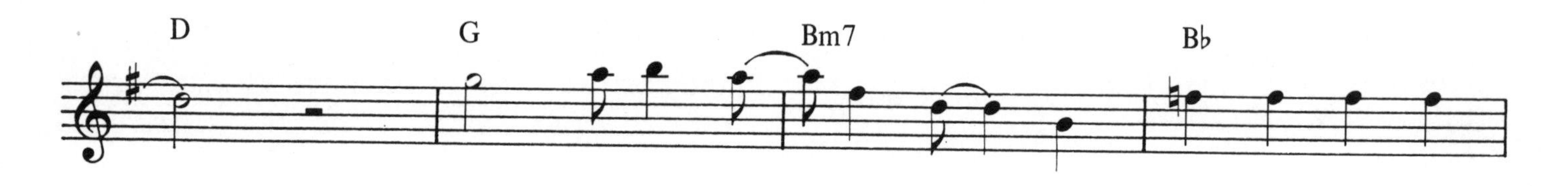

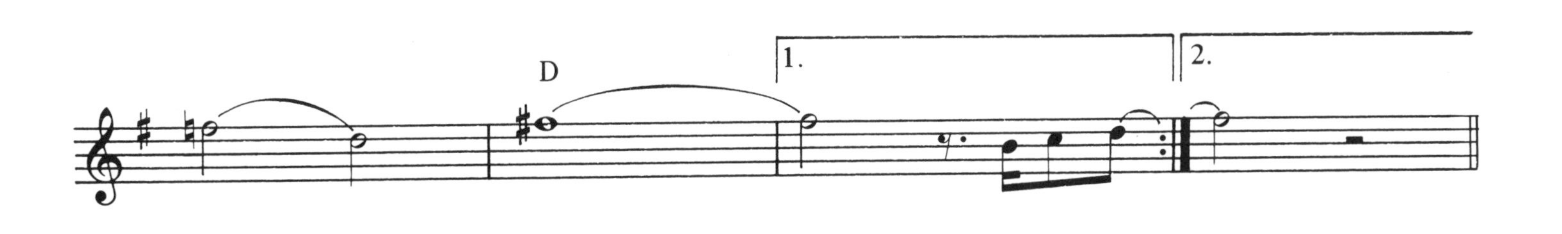
D
1.
2.

Dm
B♭
Dm
B♭

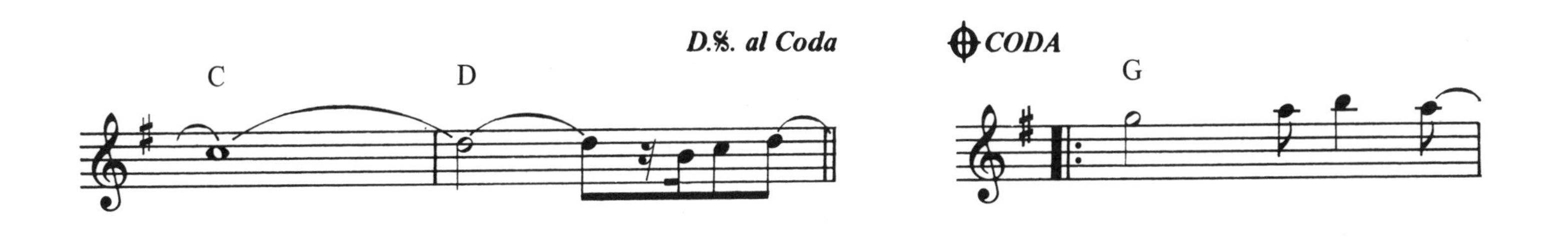
D.%. al Coda
CODA
C
D
G

Bm7
B♭
D
G

Bm7
1.
B♭
D

D
C
D
2.
B♭
D
rit.
molto rit.

Once In Royal David's City

Traditional

Past Three O'Clock

Traditional

Santa Claus Is Back In Town

Words & Music: Jerry Leiber and Mike Stoller

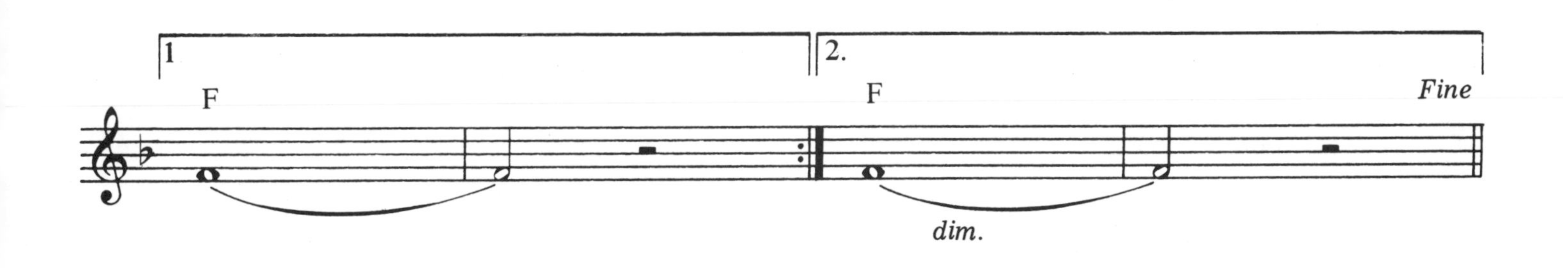

See Amid The Winter's Snow

Traditional

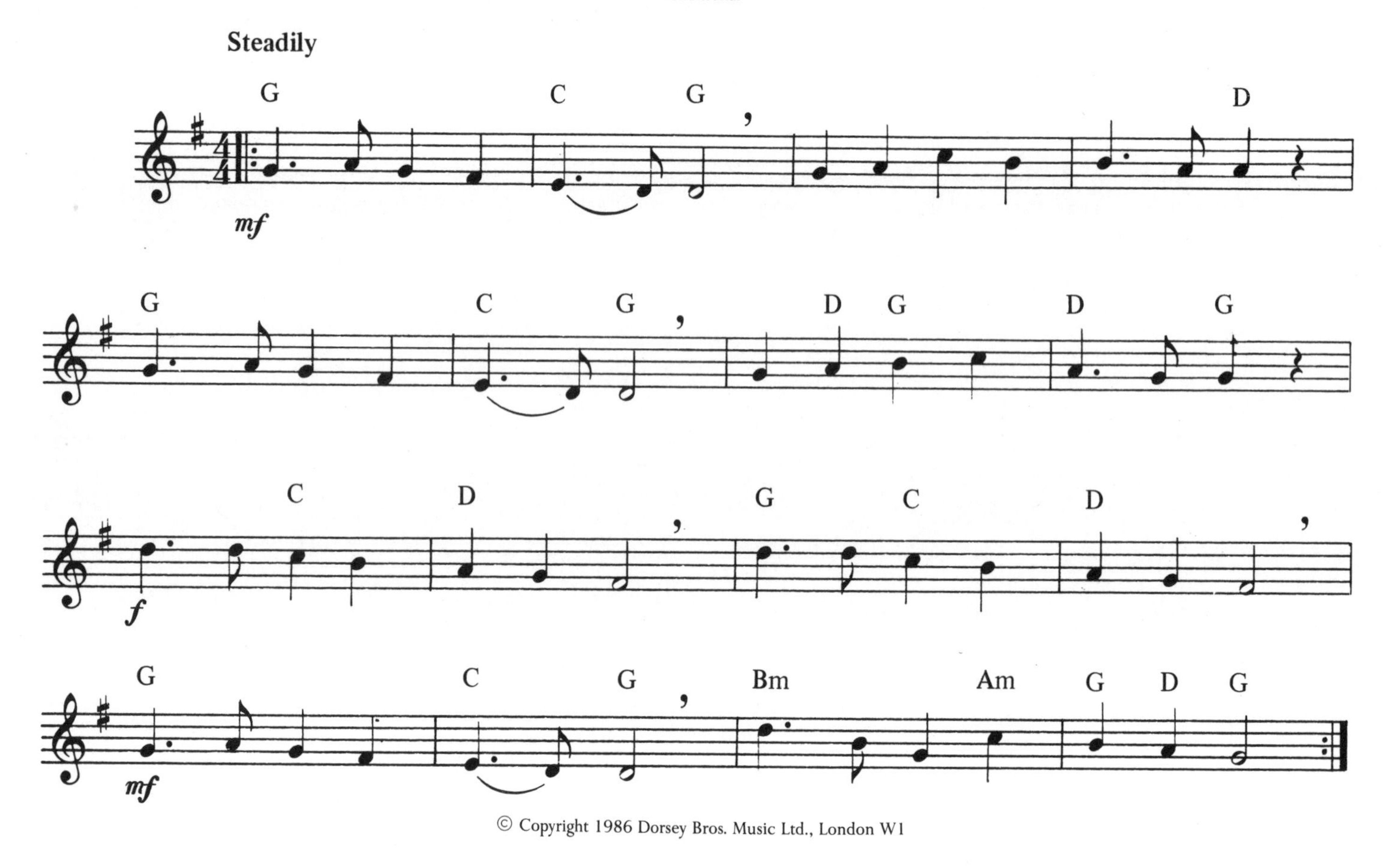

Silent Night

Traditional

Santa Claus Is Comin' To Town

Words: Haven Gillespie Music: J. Fred Coot

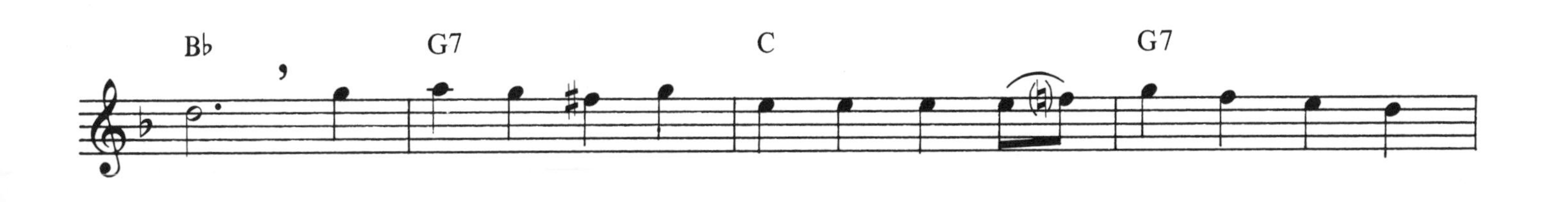

Tomorrow Shall Be My Dancing Day

Traditional

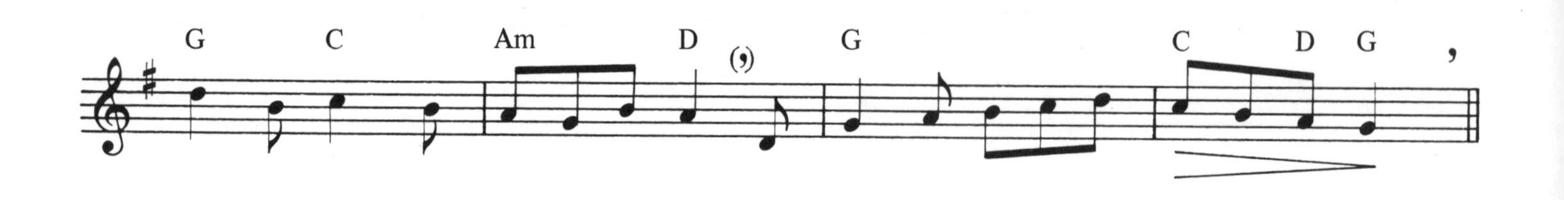

The Very First Christmas Of All

Words: Paddy Roberts   Music: Peter Hart

We Wish You A Merry Christmas

Traditional

While Shepherds Watched

Traditional

Sussex Carol

Traditional

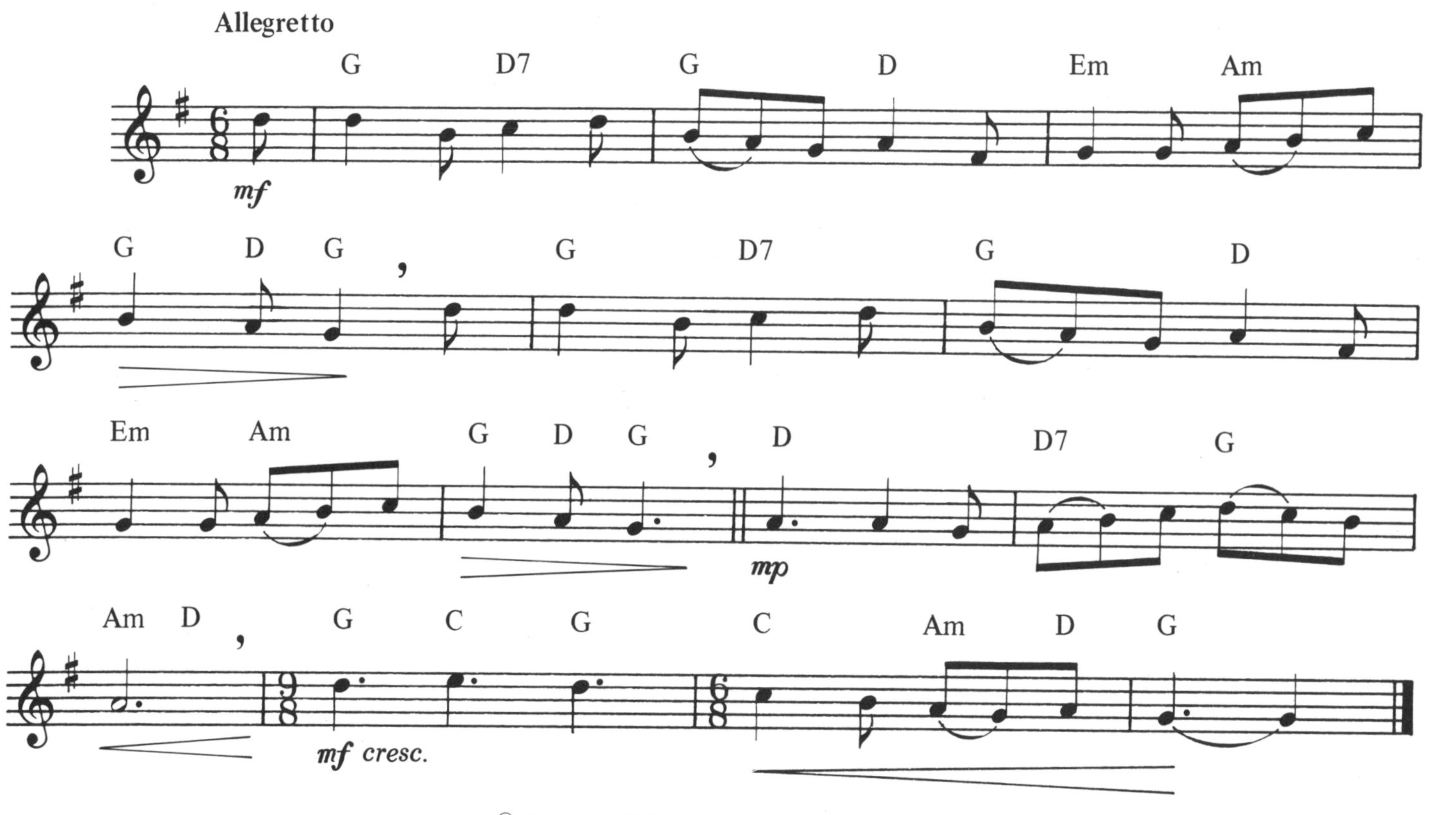

Zither Carol

Traditional

Printed in Great Britain by Printwise (Haverhill) Limited, Suffolk 8/98 (31661)

The Beatles

Enya

Phil Collins

Van Morrison

Bob Dylan

Sting

Paul Simon

Tracy Chapman

Eric Clapton

Pink Floyd

New Kids On The Block

Bryan Adams

Tina Turner

Elton John

Bee Gees

Whitney Houston

AC/DC

Bringing you the words

All the latest in rock and pop. Plus the brightest and best in West End show scores. Music books for every instrument under the sun. And exciting new teach-yourself ideas like "Let's Play Keyboard" - in cassette/book packs, or on video. Available from all good music shops.

and music

Music Sales' complete catalogue lists thousands of titles and is available free from your local music shop, or direct from Music Sales Limited. Please send a cheque or postal order for £1.50 (for postage) to:

Music Sales Limited
Newmarket Road,
Bury St Edmunds,
Suffolk IP33 3YB

Buddy

Five Guys Named Moe

Les Misérables

West Side Story

Phantom Of The Opera

Show Boat

The Rocky Horror Show

Bringing you the world's best music.